Maps·Globes·Graphs

Writer
Henry Billings

Consultants

Marian Gregory
Teacher
San Luis Coastal Unified School District
San Luis Obispo, California

Gloria Sesso
Supervisor of Social Studies
Half Hollow Hills School District
Dix Hills, New York

Norman McRae, Ph.D.
Former Director of Fine Arts and Social Studies
Detroit Public Schools
Detroit, Michigan

Edna Whitfield
Former Social Studies Supervisor
St. Louis Public Schools
St. Louis, Missouri

Marilyn Nebenzahl
Social Studies Consultant
San Francisco, California

Karen Wiggins
Director of Social Studies
Richardson Independent School District
Richardson, Texas

STECK-VAUGHN
ELEMENTARY · SECONDARY · ADULT · LIBRARY

A Harcourt Company

www.steck-vaughn.com

Acknowledgments

Editorial Director	Diane Schnell
Project Editor	Janet Jerzycki
Design Manager	Rusty Kaim
Electronic Production	UG/GGS Information Services, Inc.
Media Researcher	Claudette Landry
Cover Design	Melinda Steele
Cartography	Land Registration and Information Service
	Amherst, Nova Scotia, Canada
	Gary J. Robinson
	MapQuest.com, Inc.
	R.R. Donnelley and Sons Company

Photography Credits
COVER (globe, clouds): © PhotoDisc; p. 4 Rusty Kaim; p. 5 (both) © PhotoDisc; p. 6 (top) Rusty Kaim; p. 6 (bottom) © PhotoDisc; p. 7 (top) Park Street; p. 7 (bottom) © PhotoDisc

Illustration Credits
Dennis Harms pp. 50, 51, 55, 56; Michael Krone p. 15; Holly Cooper pp. 23, 65, 66, 67, 68, 69, 70, 71; Rusty Kaim p. 4

ISBN 0-7398-0967-9

Contents

Geography Themes 4

1 • Directions and Map Keys 8

2 • Distance and Scale 14

Geography Themes Up Close: Place 20

3 • Resource Maps 22

4 • Landform Maps 28

Geography Themes Up Close: Regions 34

5 • Route Maps 36

6 • Grids 42

Geography Themes Up Close: Movement 48

7 • Latitude 50

8 • Longitude 55

Geography Themes Up Close: Location 60

9 • Graphs 62

Geography Themes Up Close:
Human/Environment Interaction 74

Atlas 76

Glossary 79

Geography Themes

In *Maps•Globes•Graphs* you will learn about ways to study **geography**. Geography is all about Earth and how people live and work on Earth. There are five main ideas people use to study geography.

The Five Themes of Geography
- **Location**
- **Place**
- **Human/Environment Interaction**
- **Movement**
- **Regions**

Location

Location tells where something can be found. You can tell the location of something by naming what it is near or what is around it. You also can tell the location by using an address, or numbers and a street name.

 Kareem lives in this house. Tell the location of his house.

_____

_____

Place

Place tells what a location is like. Each place has **physical features**, or things from nature. These include bodies of water, landforms, weather, plants, and animals. Each place also has **human features**, such as houses, roads, bridges, schools, farms, and factories. People make these.

These pictures show two places. One picture shows the city of St. Louis. The other picture shows Yosemite National Park.

 Name a human feature of St. Louis.

_____

 Name a physical feature of Yosemite National Park.

_____

Human/Environment Interaction

Human/Environment Interaction explains how people live in their environment. **Environment** is the land, water, and air around you. It is the plant and animal life, too. How people make a living often depends on their environment. For example, people who live near the sea might fish for a living.

 How might living on the plains be different from living in the mountains?

_____

_____

_____

Human/Environment Interaction also explains how people change the environment to meet their needs and wants. People might change a field into a parking lot.

 How have people changed the environment in this picture?

_____

_____

Movement

Movement describes how people, goods, information, and ideas get from place to place. People move from place to place in cars and airplanes. How do goods move from place to place?

 How are goods moving in this picture?

_____

Information and ideas move from place to place in newspapers. Information and ideas move in other ways, too.

 How are information and ideas moving in this picture?

Regions

Regions are areas that have something in common. A region may share physical or human features. Regions can be described by such things as climate, plant life, or government. Regions can be as large as your state and as small as your community.

 What feature describes the region in this picture?

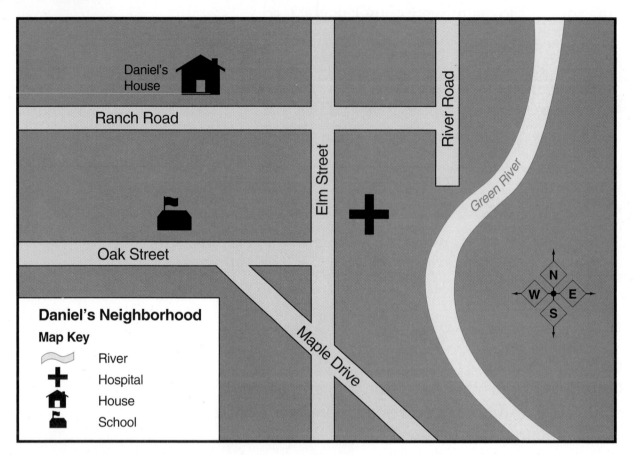

A **map** is a drawing of a real place. A map shows the place from above.

The map above shows Daniel's neighborhood. Use the map to find Daniel's house. What other things does the map show?

Follow these steps to begin reading a map.

MAP ATTACK!

- **Read the title of the map.** The title tells you what the map is about. What is the title of the map on this page?
- **Read the map key.** The map key tells you what each map **symbol** stands for. Match each symbol in the key to a symbol on the map.
- **Read the compass rose.** The compass rose tells you the directions on the map. Find places on the map that are north, south, east, and west of the hospital.

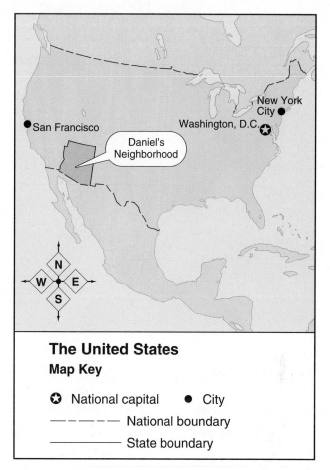

Daniel's neighborhood is in the city of Mesa. Mesa is in the state of Arizona. The map on the left shows the state of Arizona. Find Daniel's city on the map.

Arizona is in a country, the United States. The map on the right shows the United States. Find Daniel's state, Arizona.

You can see that Daniel lives in a neighborhood, a city, a state, and a country all at the same time.

Answer these questions about the map of Arizona. Use the map key and the compass rose.

► Is Mesa east or west of Phoenix?
► Is the state capital north or south of Flagstaff?

Answer these questions about the map of the United States. Use the map key and the compass rose.

► Is New York City north or south of Washington, D.C.?
► Is Arizona east or west of the national capital?

Using Symbols and Directions

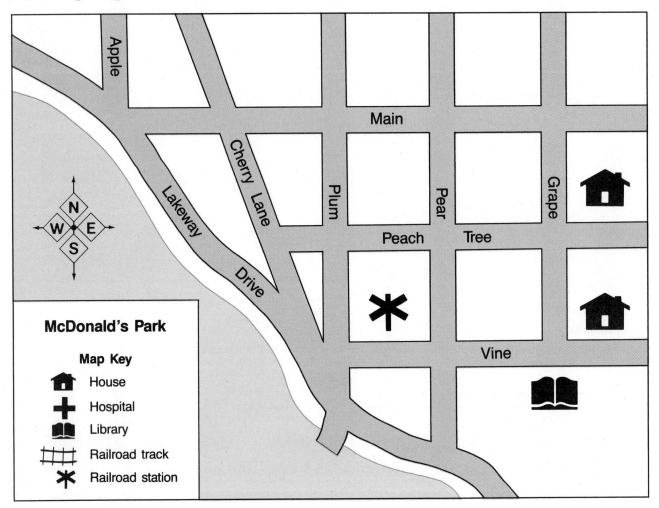

MAP ATTACK!

- **Read the title.** Write it here. _____.
- **Read the map key.** Check (✔) each symbol after you read its meaning. Check (✔) a matching symbol on the map.
- **Read the compass rose.** Circle the north arrow.

Finish the map by adding these symbols.

1. Draw a hospital north of Main between Plum and Pear.

2. Draw a house south of Peach Tree between Pear and Grape.

3. Draw a house east of Apple and north of Main.

4. Draw a railroad track down Plum , from north to south.

5. Draw a house west of Cherry Lane and south of Main.

Using Intermediate Directions

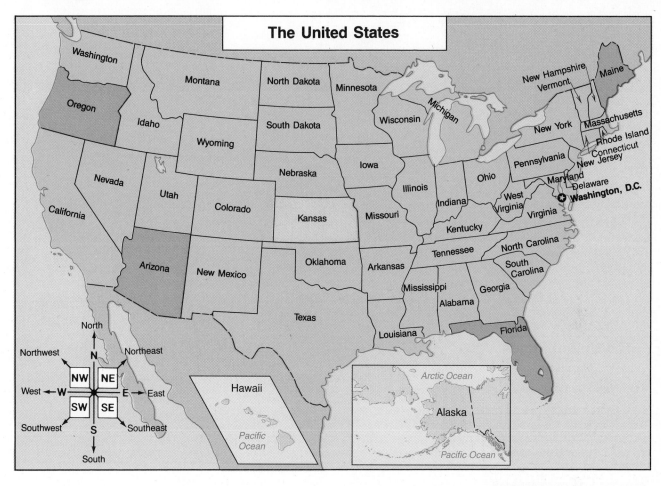

The United States

Northeast, southeast, southwest, and northwest are **intermediate directions**. They are also labeled NE, SE, SW, and NW.

1. Which direction is between north and west? _____

2. Which direction is between south and east? _____

3. Northeast is between _____ and _____ .

4. Southwest is between _____ and _____ .

5. To drive from Kansas to Oregon, you go _____ .

6. To drive from Kansas to Florida, you go _____ .

7. To drive from Kansas to Arizona, you go _____ .

8. To drive from Kansas to Maine, you go _____ .

Using Symbols and Intermediate Directions

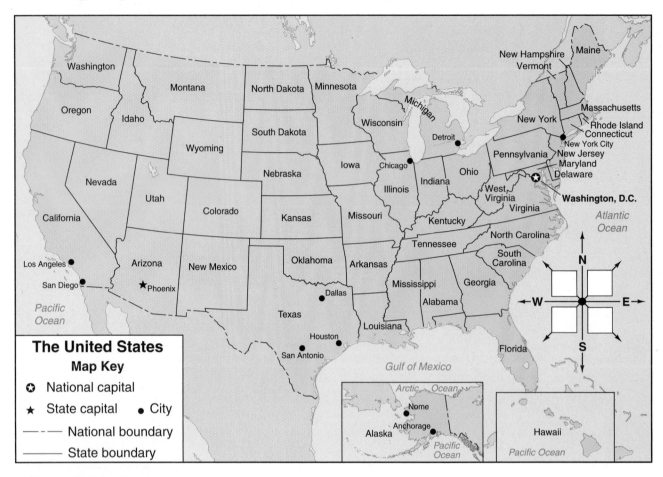

MAP ATTACK!

Follow the steps on page 8 to begin reading this map.

1. Label the intermediate directions with NE, SE, SW, and NW. Use the compass rose to find these directions.

2. To drive from Arizona to Colorado, you go _____.

3. To drive from New York to Texas, you go _____.

4. Florida is in the _____ part of the United States.

5. New Mexico is in the _____ part of the United States.

6. To drive from San Diego to Los Angeles, you go _____.

7. Chicago is in the _____ part of Illinois.

8. To drive from Nome to Anchorage, you go _____.

Skill Check

Word Check　　　**map key**　　**intermediate directions**
　　　　　　　　　　　title　　　　　　**compass rose**

Write the word that makes each sentence true.

1. The _____ _____ helps you find directions.

2. The letters NE, SE, SW, and NW stand for

   _____ _____ .

3. The name of a map is its _____ .

4. The _____ _____ explains the symbols
   on a map.

Map Reading Check

Finish the map of Farm Valley.

1. Draw an airport northwest of Indian River.

2. Draw a lake west of the park.

3. Draw a school south of the railroad near Avenue C.

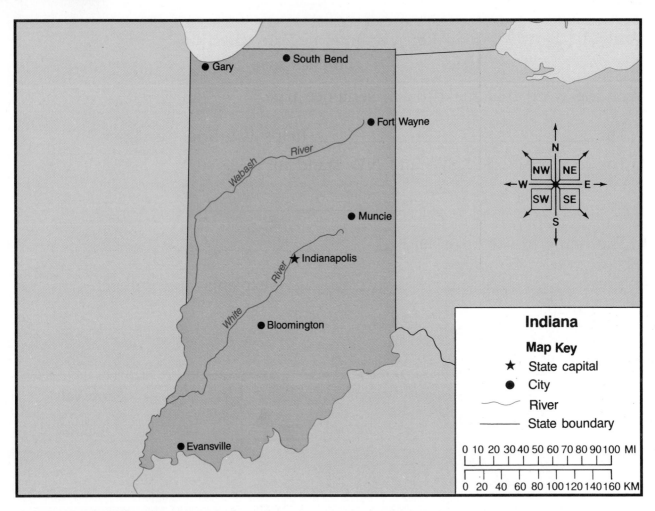

Maps show big places on small pieces of paper. Find Gary and South Bend on the map. Gary is about sixty miles from South Bend. On this map, Gary is about an inch from South Bend.

You can find **distance** on a map by reading a map scale. A **map scale** tells you how many miles in the real world equal an inch on the map.

Some map scales look like this:

```
0                              100   MI
├──────────────────────────────┤
┌──────────────────────────────┐
0                              160   KM
```

Look at the marks and numbers along the top. They stand for distance in miles. Look at the marks and numbers along the bottom. They stand for distance in kilometers. **Miles** and **kilometers** are two ways of measuring distance.

▶ Find the map scale on the Indiana map.
▶ What letters stand for miles?
▶ What letters stand for kilometers?

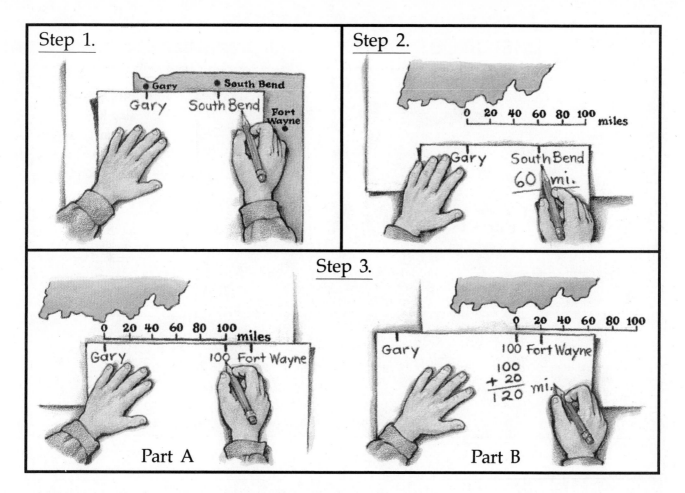

Step 1.

Step 2.

Step 3.

Part A

Part B

Suppose you want to find the distance between Gary and South Bend. Here's how to use the map scale:

Step 1. Lay the edge of a piece of paper in a straight line from Gary to South Bend. Mark your paper below each city.

Step 2. Lay the edge of your paper along the scale. Your left-hand mark should be below "0". Read the scale numbers nearest your right-hand mark. The numbers tell you that Gary and South Bend are about 60 miles apart.

Step 3. What if the distance between two cities is greater than the scale? Lay your paper on the scale and mark your paper below the highest number on the scale. Then move your paper so that your new mark is below "0". Read the scale number nearest your right-hand mark. Add that number to the highest number on the scale. The sum is your distance.

► Can you find the distance between Fort Wayne and South Bend?

Figuring Distances on a Map

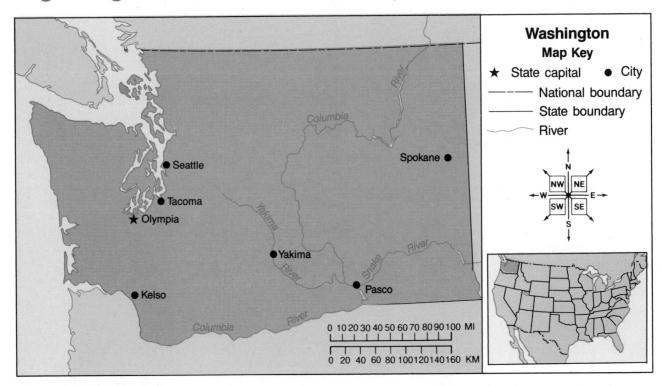

MAP ATTACK!

● The title of the map is _____.

● The state capital is _____.

● The scale goes up to _____ miles.

Use the edge of a paper and the scale to figure these distances. If your marks fall between the scale marks, try to estimate the distance. Write the distance in miles.

1. From Kelso to Seattle is about _____ miles.

2. From Seattle to Olympia is about _____ miles.

3. From Yakima to Spokane is about _____ miles.

4. From Tacoma to Spokane is about _____ miles.

5. From Olympia to Yakima is about _____ miles.

Figuring Distances

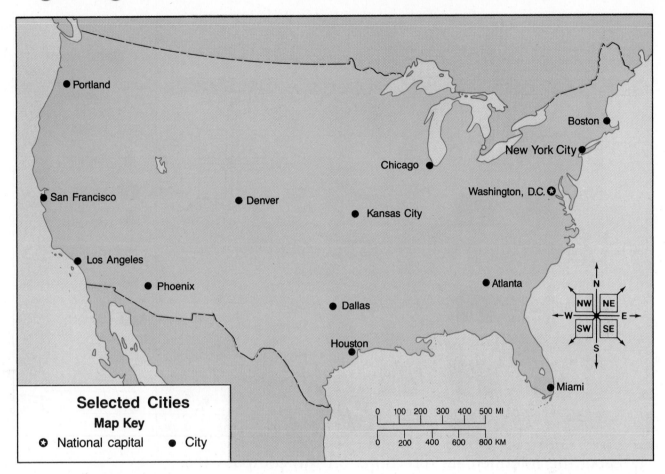

MAP ATTACK!

Follow the steps on page 8 to begin reading this map.

Use the map scale and the edge of a paper to find these distances.

1. From Phoenix to Dallas is about _____ miles.

2. From Portland to Chicago is about _____ miles.

3. From Boston to Kansas City is about _____ miles.

4. From Atlanta to Houston is about _____ miles.

5. From New York City to Miami is about _____ miles.

6. From Los Angeles to Chicago is about _____ miles.

7. From San Francisco to Denver is about _____ miles.

Reading a Map

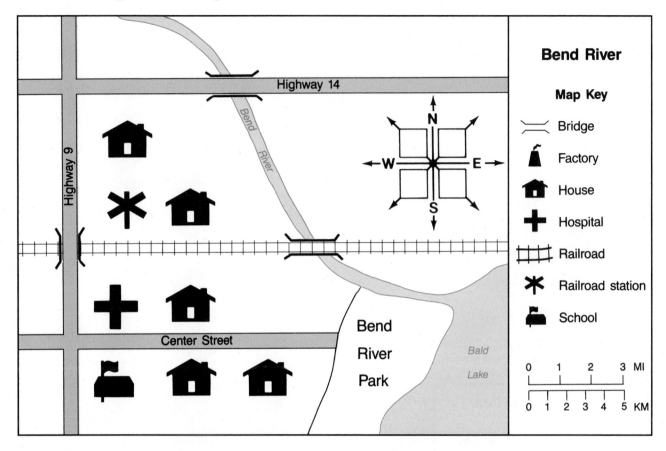

1. Label the intermediate directions on the compass rose.

2. Draw a factory northeast of the railroad station near the houses.

3. The hospital is at the corner of _____ and

   _____ .

Name the direction that finishes the sentence.

4. The railroad station is _____ of the river.

5. The Bend River runs _____ toward the lake.

6. The school is _____ of the hospital.

Use the map scale and the edge of a piece of paper to find these distances.

7. The railroad bridge over Bend River is about _____ miles long.

8. From Highway 14 to Center Street is about _____ miles.

Skill Check

Word Check   **map scale   distance**
                                       miles   kilometers

Use each word to finish a sentence. Use one word twice.

1. _____ is how far apart places are.

2. A _____ is used to figure distances on a map.

3. Kilometers and miles measure _____ on Earth.

4. The letters **KM** stand for _____ .

5. The letters **MI** stand for _____ .

Map Scale Check

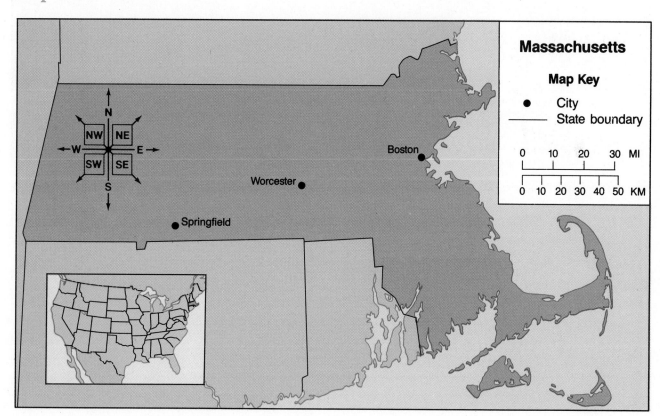

Use the scale and a piece of paper to find these distances.

1. Springfield is about _____ miles from Worcester.

2. Boston is about _____ miles from Springfield.

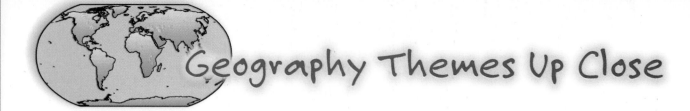

Geography Themes Up Close

Place describes a location. Are there hills there? What kinds of buildings are there? The physical and human features of each place make it special.

1. What store is north of the bookstore?

   _____

2. List three features of Oak Mall.

   _____

   _____

3. Find the toy store on the map. Circle it. Mark **P** on it if it is a physical feature. Mark **H** if it is a human feature.

4. Find the fairgrounds on the map above. They are west of Fox Lake. Label them on the map. Mark **P** if they are a physical feature. Mark **H** if they are a human feature.

5. Name a physical feature of Meg's community. Mark it with **P** on the map.

_____

6. What features in Meg's community make it different from your community?

_____

_____

_____

3 Resource Maps

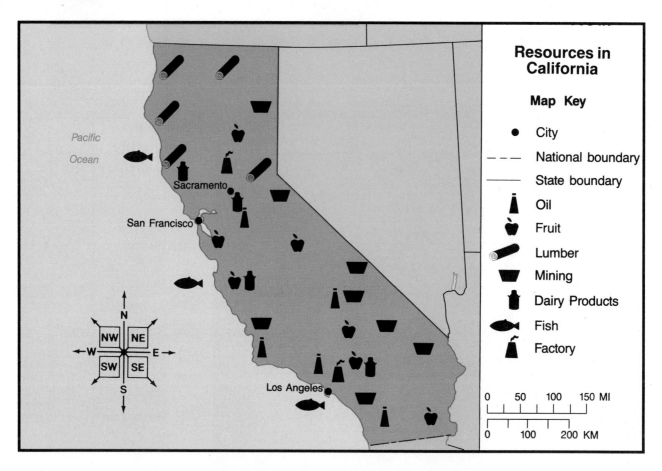

This map shows the resources in California. **Resources** are things people can use. The map also shows the areas where those resources are found. Find the factory symbols on the map. A **factory** is a place where resources are made into other things.

Use your map attack skills to begin reading this map.

MAP ATTACK!

- **Read the title.** The title tells you the purpose of the map and what the map shows.
- **Study the key.** Read the meanings of the symbols. Find each symbol on the map. Which resources are near cities? Which are on land? Which are in water?
- **Read the compass rose.** Find north on the map. Which resources are in the north? in the south? in the east? in the west? in the center?

The resources you see on the map on page 22 can be grouped in different ways. Grouping them makes them easier to study and remember. Some of the resources come from animals. Some come from plants. Others are minerals found in the earth. This table shows California's resources listed in the three groups.

California's Resources		
Animal Resources	Plant Resources	Mineral Resources
dairy products	fruit	mining
fish	lumber	oil

Resources can also be grouped by place. Which symbols are mainly in the north? in the south? in the east? in the west? This table shows California's resources by place.

California's Resources by Place	
Resources mainly in the east:	mining ◾ fruit 🍎
Resources mainly in the west:	fishing 🐟 dairy products 🍶
Resources mainly in the north:	lumber 🪵
Resources mainly in the south:	oil ▲

Reading a Resource Map

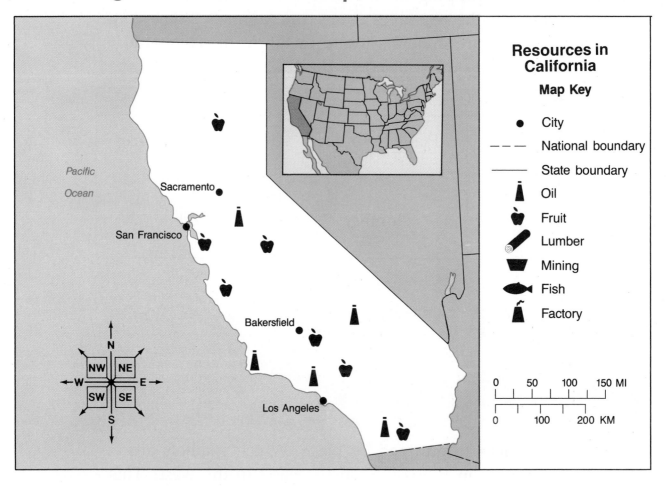

Follow the four steps to begin reading this map.

MAP ATTACK!

- **Read the title.** Write it here. _____
- **Read the map key.** Check (✔) each symbol after you read its meaning. Check (✔) a matching symbol on the map.
- **Read the compass rose.** Circle the north arrow.
- **Read the map scale.** Circle the names of the two ways distance is measured on the map scale.

1. Draw four factory symbols, one each near San Francisco, Los Angeles, Bakersfield, and Sacramento.

2. Draw three mining symbols along California's eastern boundary.

3. Draw three fishing symbols off the western coastline.

4. Draw three lumber symbols near the northern boundary.

Reading a Resource Map

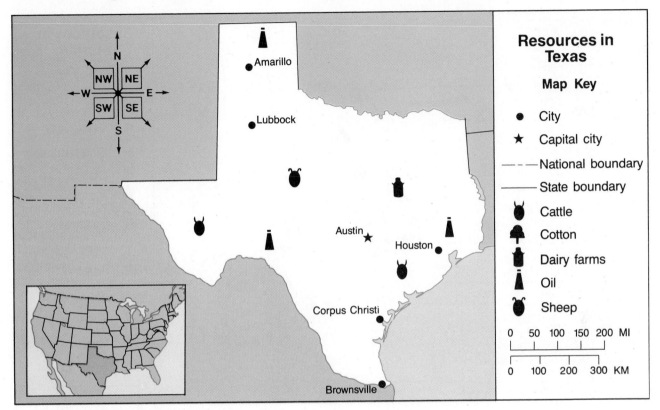

Resources in Texas

Map Key

- ● City
- ★ Capital city
- --- National boundary
- — State boundary
- Cattle
- Cotton
- Dairy farms
- Oil
- Sheep

0 50 100 150 200 MI

0 100 200 300 KM

MAP ATTACK!

● The title of the map is _____ .

● The state capital is _____ .

● The distance from Austin to Houston is _____ miles.

1. Draw a cotton symbol southwest of Corpus Christi.

2. Draw one cotton symbol north of Austin, one north of Lubbock, and one north of Brownsville.

3. Draw two oil symbols, one near Lubbock and one near Houston.

4. Draw two cattle symbols, one northwest of Amarillo, and one northwest of Austin.

5. Circle the resource that is produced in more places.

cotton or dairy   sheep or cattle   oil or cotton

Reading a Resource Map

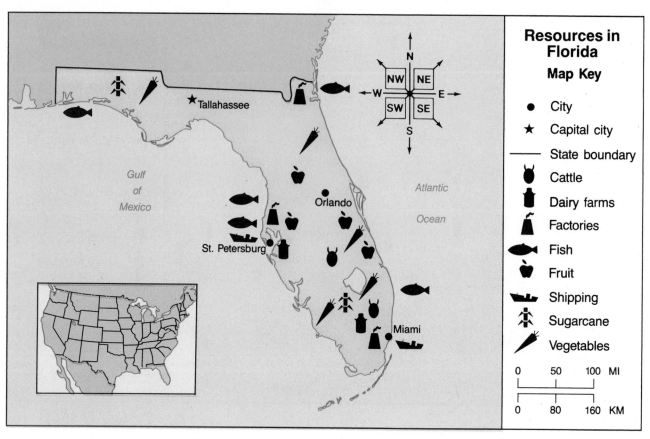

Resources in Florida

Map Key

- •   City
- ★   Capital city
- ——   State boundary
- Cattle
- Dairy farms
- Factories
- Fish
- Fruit
- Shipping
- Sugarcane
- Vegetables

0   50   100   MI

0   80   160   KM

1. What does the map show? (What is the title?)

_____

2. Circle Florida on the small U.S. map. Is Florida in the northern

or southern U.S.? _____

Use the map scale and the edge of a piece of paper to find these distances.

3. From St. Petersburg to Orlando is about _____ miles.

4. From St. Petersburg to Miami is about _____ miles.

5. Which cities are on the coast?

_____   _____

6. Name three of the most important resources in Florida.

_____   _____   _____

Skill Check

Word Check   **factory**   **resource**

Write the word that makes each sentence true.

1. A _____ is something that people use.

2. Resources are made into other things at a _____.

Resource Map Check

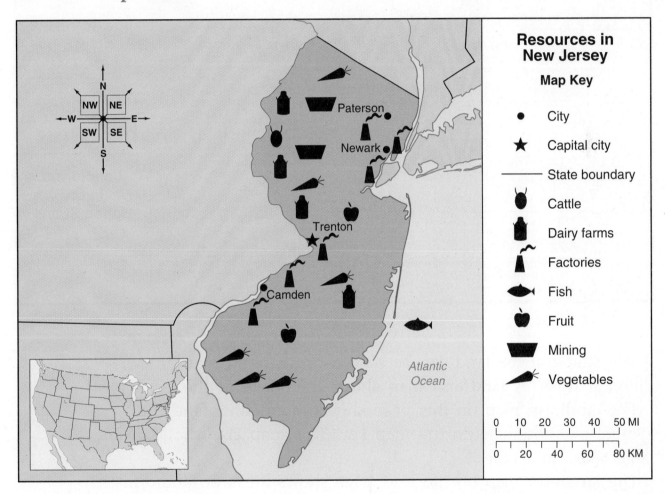

1. Cattle and dairy farms are mainly in the _____ part of New Jersey.

2. The main resource in the south is _____.

3. Circle the resource that is produced in more places.

     cattle or dairy   fruit or fish   mining or vegetables

4. What are located near the cities? _____

4 Landform Maps

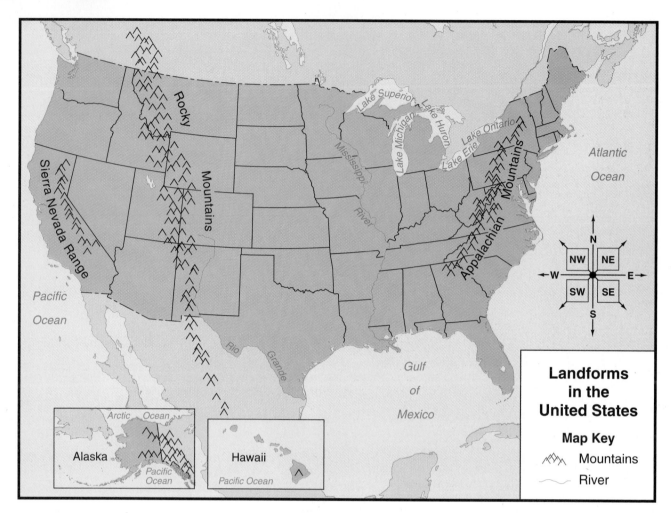

Map A

The shape of the land can be shown on maps in many different ways. A **landform map** shows the shape of the land.

The landform map on this page shows mountains. Find the symbol for mountains in the map key. This map also shows rivers, large lakes, and oceans.

The landform map on the next page shows areas of landforms. The areas are different colors. The highest landform is the darkest color. Which landform is highest? The lowest landform is the lightest color. These are **plains**, or flat lands.

Find the areas of plateaus. A **plateau** is high, flat land.

Find the Gulf of Mexico. A **gulf** is a large body of water that cuts deep into the land.

Land next to the ocean is called the **coast**. What states have some coast?

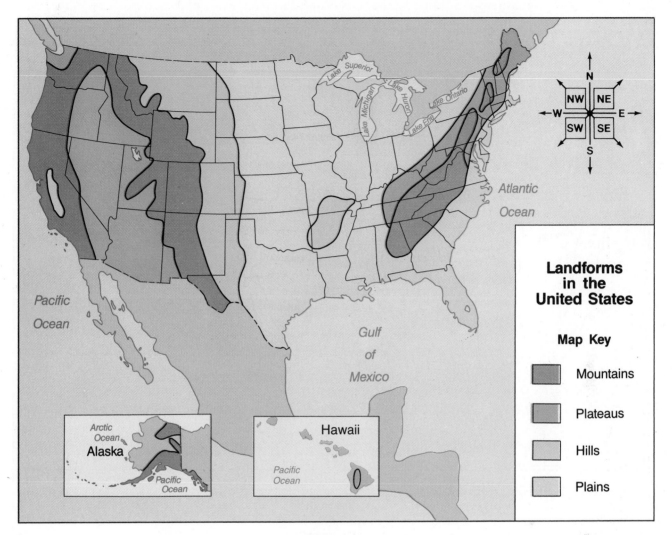

Map B

Compare Map A and Map B.

1. What landforms are only on Map B? _____

_____

2. What bodies of water are only on Map A? _____

3. Are there more mountains in the eastern or the western

   United States? _____

4. Where are most of the plains? _____

5. What landform is on the west coast? _____

6. Circle the label for a gulf on both maps.

Making and Using a Landform Map

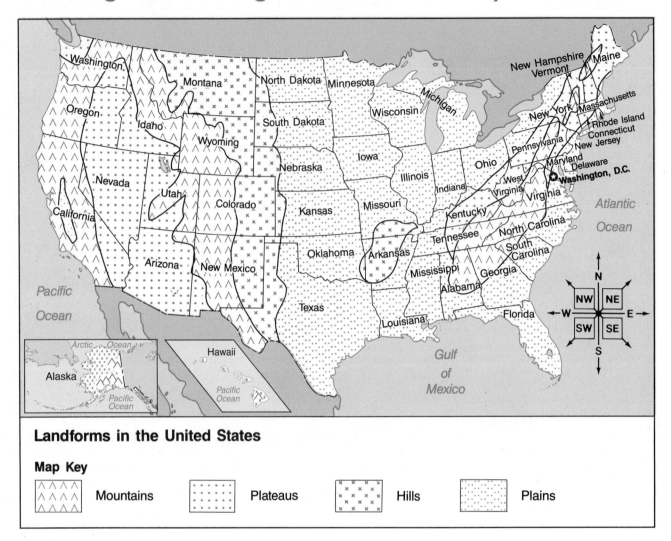

Landforms in the United States

Map Key

Mountains Plateaus Hills Plains

MAP ATTACK!

- **Read the title.** Write it here. _____
- **Read the compass rose.** Circle the intermediate direction arrows.

1. Color the map key. Use colored pens or pencils.
   Choose four colors for the landform areas.

2. Color the map to match the key.

3. Which landform(s) does your state have? _____

Reading a Landform Map

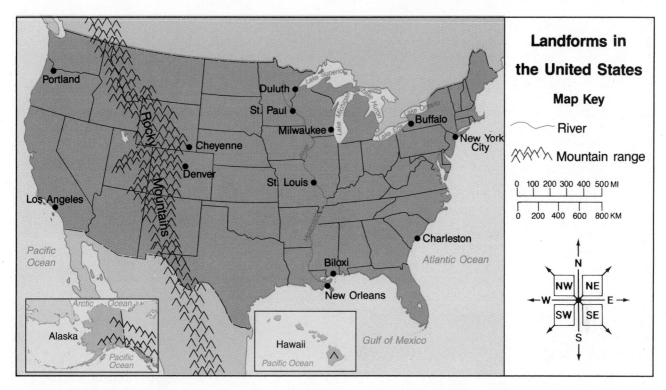

MAP ATTACK!

● The title of the map is _____ .

● From New York City to Buffalo is about _____ miles.

1. Name a city on the west coast. _____

2. Name a city on the east coast. _____

3. Name a city on the Gulf of Mexico coast. _____

4. Name two cities on the edge of the Great Lakes.

_____   _____

5. Name two cities on the eastern edge of the Rocky Mountains.

_____   _____

6. Name two cities on the Mississippi River.

_____   _____

Making and Using a Landform Map

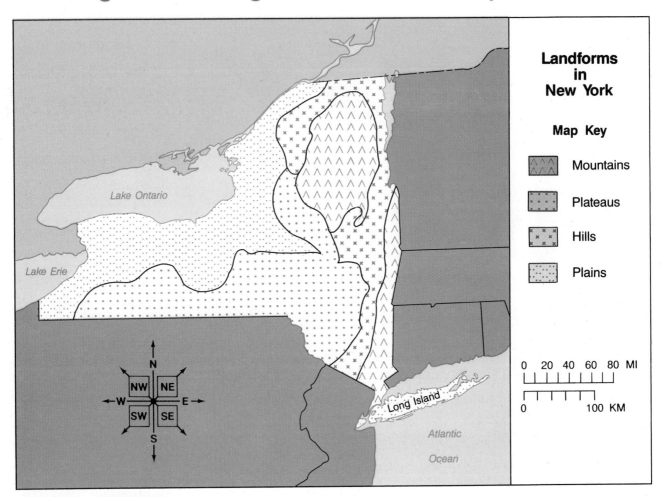

MAP ATTACK!

Follow the steps on page 24 to begin reading this map.

1. Color the landform areas to match the key.
   Use colored pencils or pens.

2. New York's plains are mostly in the _____ .

3. New York's mountains are mostly in the _____ .

4. What lakes form part of New York's western boundary?

   _____   _____

5. Long Island is about _____ miles long.

6. Lake Ontario is about _____ miles long (east to west).

Skill Check

Word Check   **plateau**   **gulf**

                         coast   **landform map**

Write the word that makes each sentence true.

1. A _____ is high, flat land.

2. A _____ is a large body of water that cuts deep into the land.

3. A _____ is land next to the ocean.

Landform Map Check

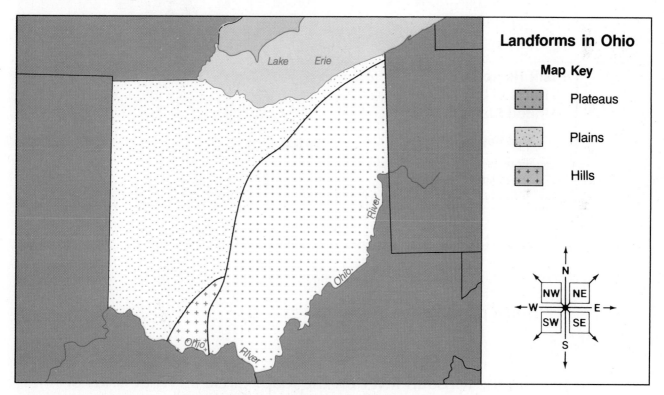

1. Color the landform areas to match the key.

2. Ohio's plains are mostly in which direction? _____

   Ohio's plateaus are mostly in the _____ .

3. What lake forms part of Ohio's northern boundary? _____

4. What river forms Ohio's southern boundary? _____

Geography Themes Up Close

Regions are areas that share the same feature. The map below shows plant regions in the United States.

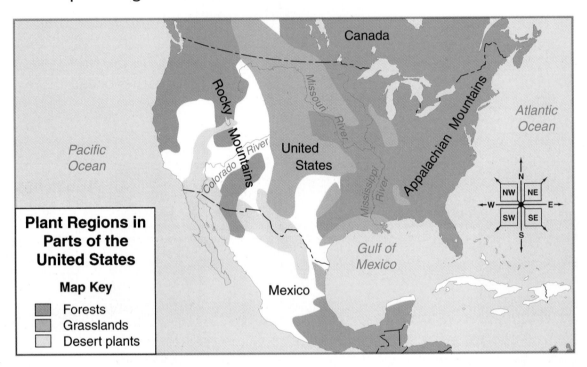

1. What three plant regions are shown on this map?

   _____

2. Which plant region is largest?

   _____

3. Find the Missouri River on the map. Circle it. What kinds of plants mostly grow along the Missouri River?

   _____

4. What kinds of plants grow along the border of the United States and Mexico?

   _____

The map shows Desmond Park—one of ten community parks in Elm City. All the parks in Elm City have the same features.

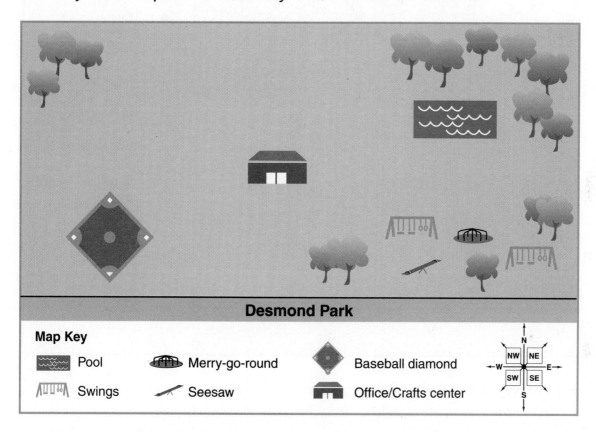

Desmond Park

Map Key

≈≈≈ Pool   ⊕ Merry-go-round   ◆ Baseball diamond

⋀⊔⊔⋀ Swings   ╱ Seesaw   ⬛ Office/Crafts center

Compass: N, NW, NE, W, E, SW, SE, S

5. There are tennis courts north of the baseball diamond. Mark **TC** on the map for the tennis courts.

6. What direction is the pool from the baseball diamond?

    _____

7. What activity is held in the Desmond Park office building?

    _____

8. Why do you think the parks in Elm City form a region?

    _____

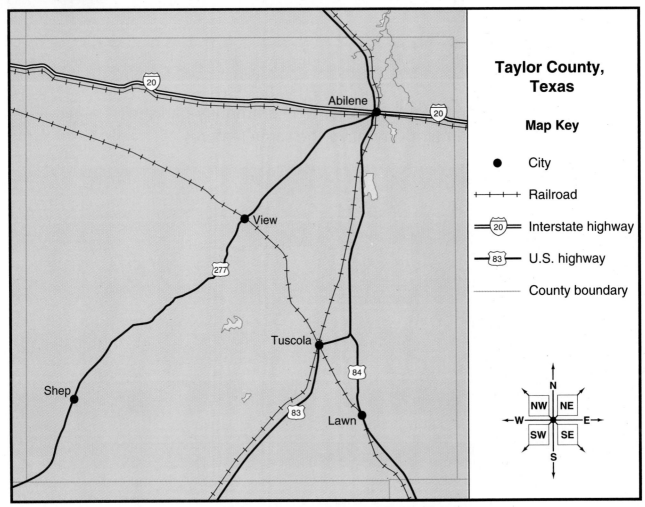

A **route** is a way of getting from one place to another. There are many different kinds of routes. Roads and railroads are routes. What are some other kinds of routes?

The map on this page shows routes. What different kinds of routes does the map show?

▶ Study the map key. What does each symbol stand for?

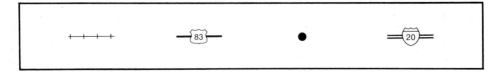

▶ Which city has the most routes going through it?
▶ Which route goes through Shep?
▶ Which routes go through Tuscola?
▶ Which route runs along Interstate highway 20?

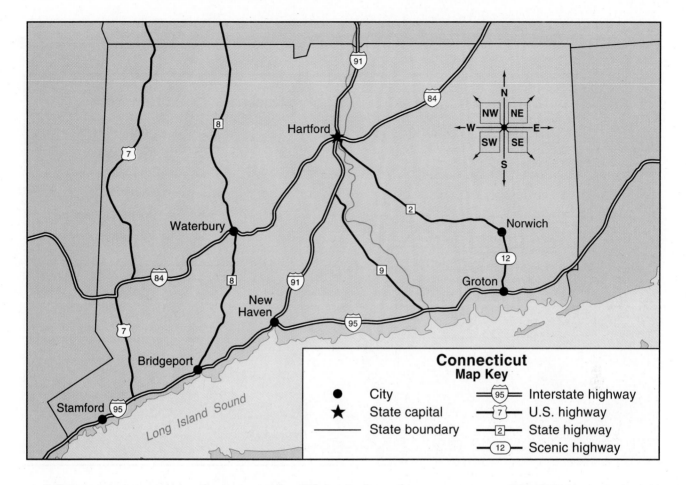

Most route maps show roads. This is because most routes are roads. Look at the map above. It shows main roads in Connecticut. Main roads are called **highways**.

Not all highways are the same. How many different kinds of highways do you see on the map? The map key tells you how the different kinds of highways are marked on the map.

► Study the map key. Find the symbol for a state highway. Find a state highway on the map.

► Find the symbol for a scenic highway. Find a scenic highway on the map.

► What kind of highway goes from Waterbury to Hartford?

► What kind of highway goes from Hartford to Norwich?

► What kind of highway goes along the water?

► What two cities does the scenic highway go through?

► What kind of highway is Highway 7?

► Which highway would you take from Hartford to New Haven?

Reading a Route Map

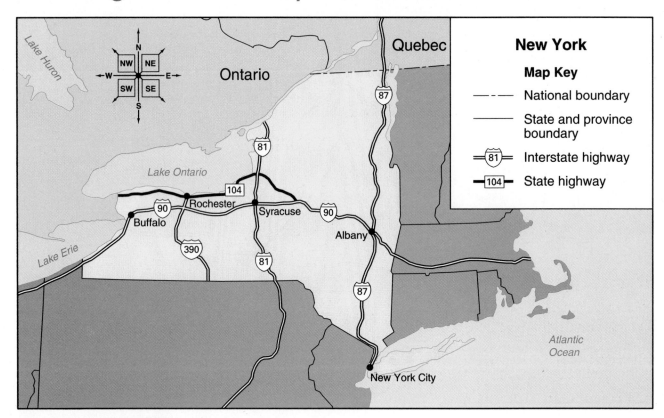

MAP ATTACK!

- **Read the title.** Write it here. _____
- **Read the key.** There are two types of highways. An **interstate highway** goes through more than one state. A **state highway** does not.
- **Read the compass rose.** Circle the arrow that points north.

1. How many interstate highways are in New York? _____

2. What highway runs along the coast of Lake Ontario? _____

3. What cities are along Highway 90? _____

   _____   _____

4. What highway goes south from Syracuse? _____

5. What highway would take you into Quebec, Canada? _____

Reading a Route Map

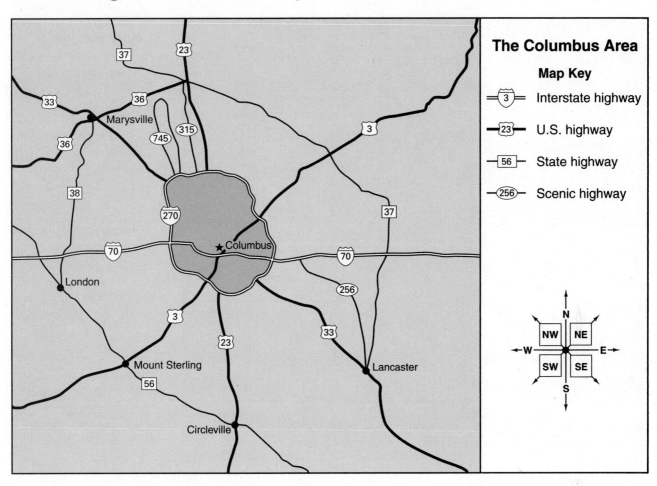

1. What highway goes around Columbus? _____

2. What highways would take you into downtown Columbus?

   _____   _____

3. Scenic Highway 256 connects Interstate 70 with what city?

   _____

4. Which scenic highway begins and ends at Interstate 270? _____

5. If you travelled from Circleville to Marysville on Highways 56 and 38, what cities would you drive through?

   _____   _____

6. What highways would you take from Lancaster to Marysville

   without going to Columbus? _____   _____

Reading a Route and Landform Map

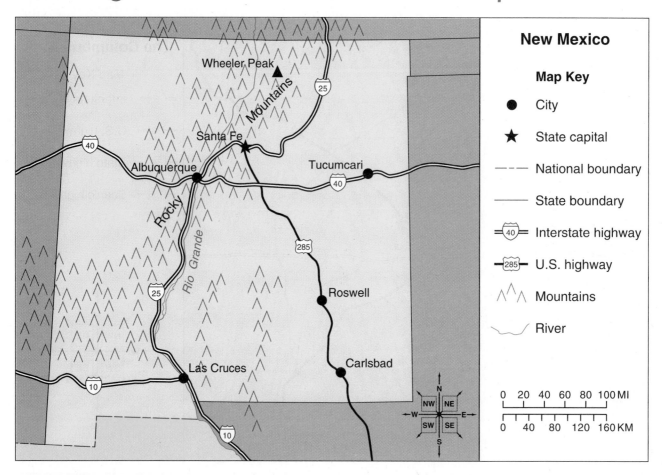

New Mexico

Map Key

- City
- ★ State capital
- --- National boundary
- — State boundary
- =40= Interstate highway
- 285 U.S. highway
- ∧∧∧ Mountains
- ∿ River

0 20 40 60 80 100 MI

0 40 80 120 160 KM

MAP ATTACK!

Follow the steps on page 38 to begin reading this map.

1. What three interstate highways go through New Mexico?

   _____

2. Circle the city that is in the mountains.

   Santa Fe   Roswell   Carlsbad

3. What kind of highway is Highway 285? _____

4. To drive from Roswell to Carlsbad, which direction should

   you go? _____ About how far is it? _____

5. What two cities are on the Rio Grande?

   _____

Skill Check

route

Use <u>route</u> in a sentence that shows its meaning.

_____

Route Map Check

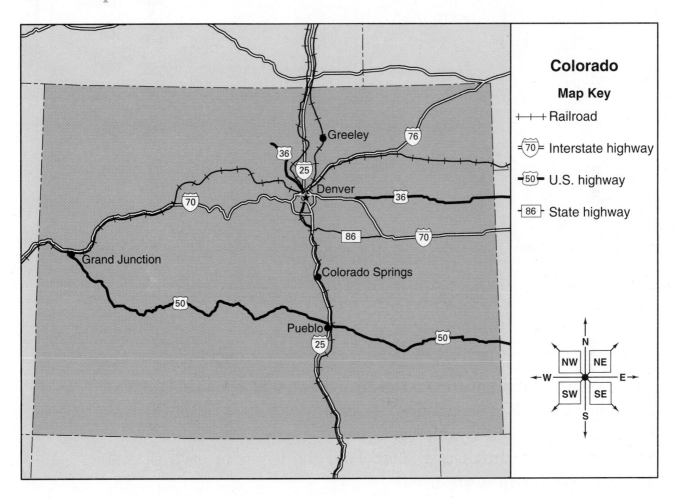

1. What routes can you take between Greeley and Grand Junction?

   _____

2. Which city has the most routes leading to it? _____

3. Which interstate highways lead to Denver? _____

4. Which U.S. highway leads to Denver? _____

5. Which state highway leads to Denver? _____

6 Grids

Sometimes you want to say exactly where a place is on a map. You can do this by using a grid. A **grid** is a pattern of lines that cross each other. The lines form squares.

Each row of squares has a letter. Find the letters at each side of the map. What letters are used?

Each column of squares has a number. Find the numbers across the top and the bottom of the map. What numbers are used?

Each square on the map is named with a letter and a number.

Here is how to find square A-2. Put your finger on the letter A. Move your finger across the row. Stop when you come to column 2. This is square A-2.

► Can you find square C-3?

► In which square is the store?

► Which squares does the railroad go through?

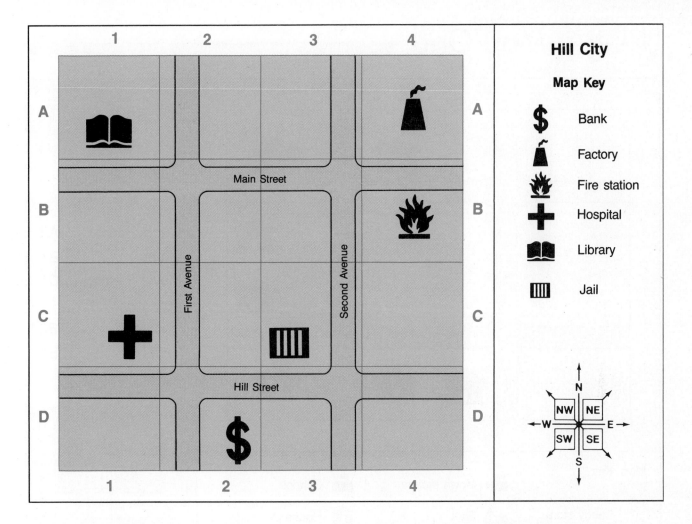

A **map index** is an alphabetical list of places on the map. The index tells in which square you can find each place. Suppose you need to find the hospital. Look under H in the index below. Read the letter and number of the square next to the word <u>hospital</u>.

Now find the hospital on the map. Put your finger on C. Move across that row until you are in column 1. The hospital is in square C-1.

Complete this index by finding the square for each place.

<u>Map Index</u>

Bank _____   Fire Station _____   Jail _____

Factory _____   Hospital   **C-1**   Library _____

Using a Map Grid

1. What city does this map show? _____

2. Study the map index.
   Draw the buildings from the index on the map where they belong.

3. What street runs through squares A-1, A-2, A-3, and A-4?

   _____

4. What street runs through squares A-3, B-3, and C-3?

   _____

5. What building is in square C-3? _____

6. Which square has the most buildings in it? _____

Using a Map Grid

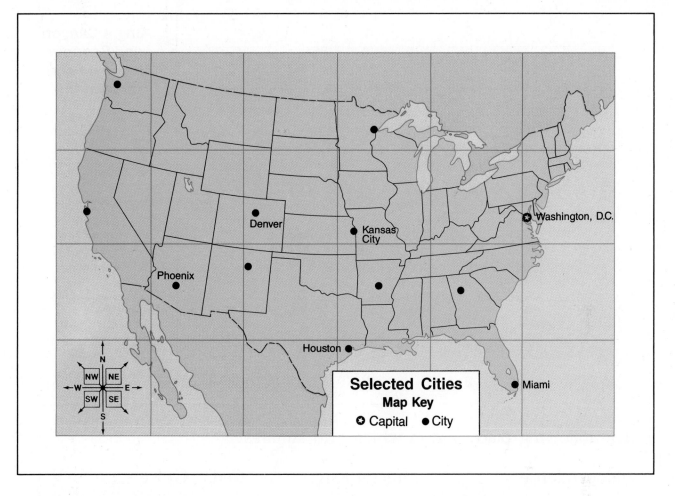

1. Finish the grid. Write the letters A, B, C, and D down each side. Write the numbers 1, 2, 3, 4, 5, and 6 across the top and bottom.

2. In which square is each place?

Washington, D.C. _____   Miami _____

Houston _____   Phoenix _____

Denver _____   Kansas City _____

3. Find these cities on the map. Label each city.
   San Francisco B-1   Olympia A-1   Little Rock C-4
   Duluth   A-4   Santa Fe C-3   Atlanta   C-5

4. If you drove from Denver to Washington, D.C., what

   squares would you drive in? _____ _____ _____ _____

Using a Map Grid

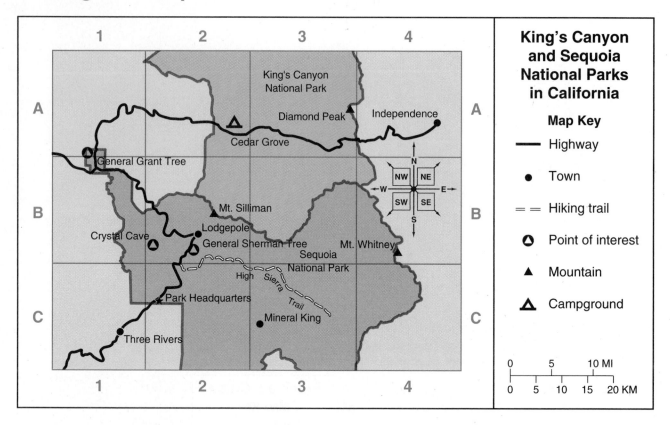

1. The following places are in which grid squares?

   Independence ____   Mineral King ____   Cedar Grove ____

   Park Headquarters ____   Mt. Silliman ____   Mt. Whitney ____

2. High Sierra Trail goes through which squares? ____ ____ ____

3. Complete this table. Use the map scale to find the distance.
   Use the compass rose to find the direction.

	Direction	Miles
►from Lodgepole to Diamond Peak	NE	____
►from General Sherman Tree to General Grant Tree	_____	____
►from Independence to Cedar Grove	_____	____
►from Crystal Cave to Park Headquarters	_____	____

Skill Check

Word Check   **grid**   **index**

Write the word that best completes each sentence.

1. A _____ is a pattern of lines that cross each other.

2. A map _____ is an alphabetical list of places on
   the map.

Map Check

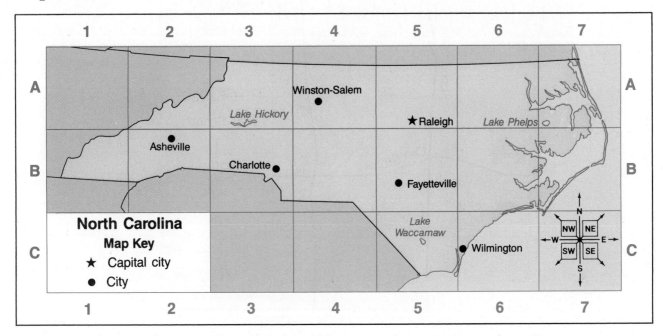

1. Name North Carolina's capital and the letter and number of

   its grid square. _____ _____

2. Complete the map index below.

_____ B-2		Lake Phelps	_____
Charlotte	_____	Lake Waccamaw	_____
Fayetteville	_____	Wilmington	_____
_____ A-3		_____ A-4	

Movement explains how people, goods, and ideas get from one place to another. Movement also tells how people in a community depend on people in other communities for goods and services.

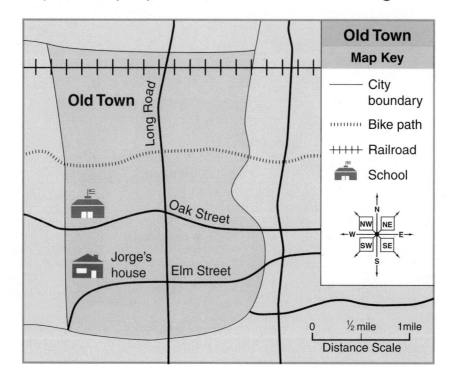

1. The map above shows Old Town where Jorge and his family live. Find Jorge's house on the map and circle it.

2. Name three kinds of transportation routes in Old Town.

   _____

3. What route would Jorge's mother take to drive him to school?

   _____

4. Jorge's family likes to ride on the bike path. How far is the bike path from Jorge's house?

   _____

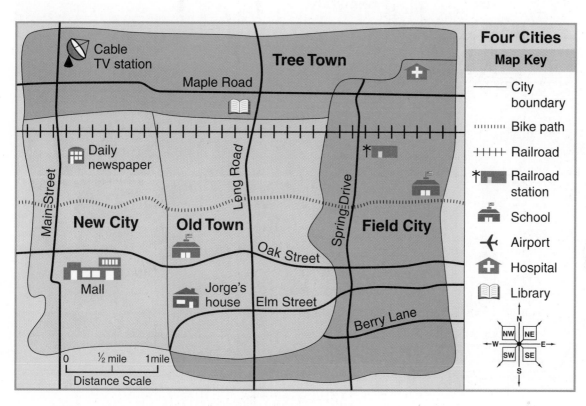

5. Where can Jorge go to shop at stores?

_____

6. Name two ways ideas move in these communities.

_____

7. Where can Jorge and his family go to get on the train?

_____

8. The people in the four communities want an airport. Draw a
   symbol on the map where you would put the airport. Tell why
   this would be a good place to build an airport.

_____

_____

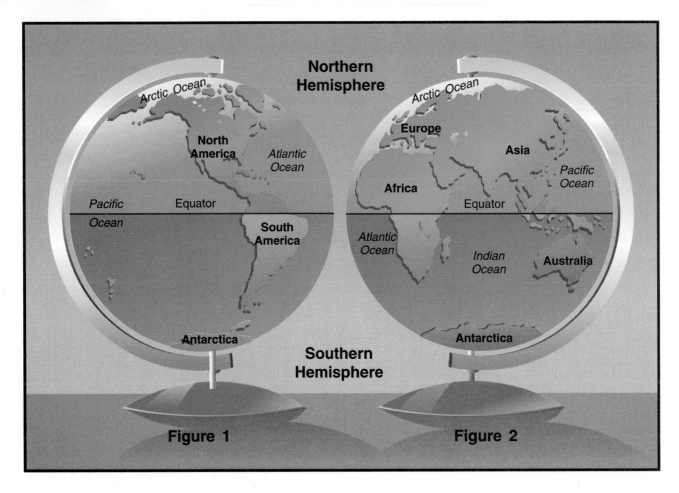

Figure 1   Figure 2

One of the most important lines on the globe is the **Equator**. The Equator is an imaginary line that goes around the middle of Earth. Study Figure 1 and Figure 2. Find the Equator on both sides of the globe.

The Equator divides the globe into two halves. Each half is called a **hemisphere**. Half the globe north of the Equator is the **Northern Hemisphere**. Half the globe south of the Equator is the **Southern Hemisphere**.

► Look at Figure 1.
   Find the land in the Northern Hemisphere. It is colored green.
   Find the land in the Southern Hemisphere. It is colored brown.

► Look at Figure 2.
   One continent is both north and south of the Equator.
   Look for the continent that is both green and brown.
   What is the name of that continent?

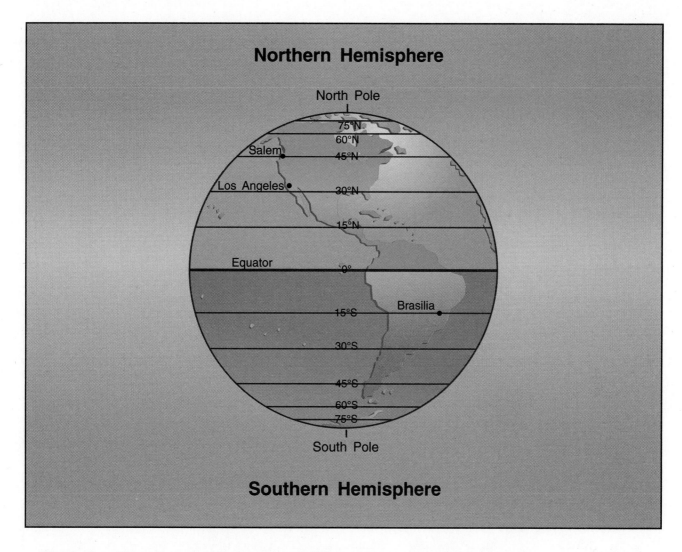

Northern Hemisphere

North Pole

75°N
60°N
Salem • 45°N
Los Angeles • 30°N
15°N
Equator 0°
15°S Brasilia •
30°S
45°S
60°S
75°S

South Pole

Southern Hemisphere

Find the Equator on the globe above. Now find the lines above and below the Equator. These are called **lines of latitude**. We use lines of latitude to locate places north and south of the Equator.

Lines of latitude are marked by **degrees**. The symbol ° stands for degrees. The Equator is at 0° latitude.

► Look at the Northern Hemisphere.
  Find the 45° North latitude line.
  What city is at 45° North?

► Look at the Southern Hemisphere.
  Find the 15° South latitude line.
  What city is at 15° South?

► Look at the whole globe.
  Find Los Angeles.
  What line of latitude is it near?

Finding Latitude

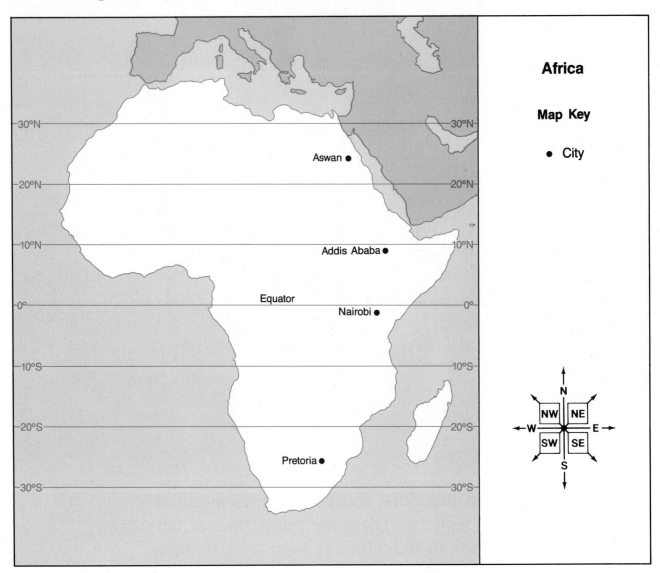

1. Color Africa green between 20°N and 30°N.

   What city lies in that area? _____

2. Color Africa brown between 0° and 10°N.

   What city lies in that area? _____

3. Color Africa yellow between 0° and 10°S.

   What city lies in that area? _____

4. Color Africa orange between 20°S and 30°S.

   What city lies in that area? _____

Finding Latitude

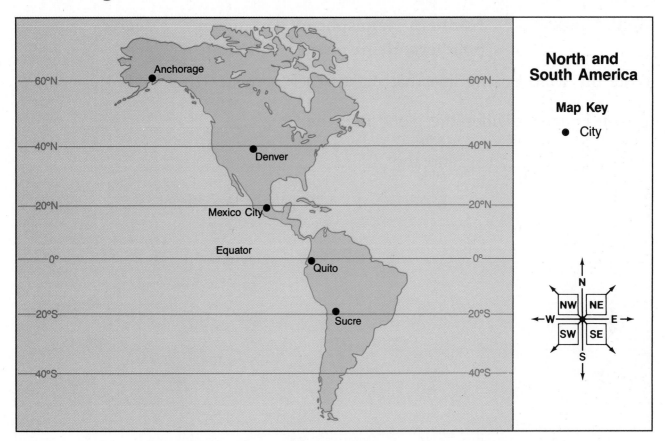

You can find a place if you know which line of latitude it is on. Every city on this map is on a line of latitude.

1. Find the Equator. Trace it in red.

   What city is on the Equator? _____

2. Find the 20°South line of latitude. Trace it in green.

   What city is at 20°South? _____

3. Find the 20°North line of latitude. Trace it in purple.

   What city is at 20°North? _____

4. Find the 40°North line of latitude. Trace it in orange.

   What city is at 40°North? _____

5. Find the 60°North line of latitude. Trace it in blue.

   What city is at 60°North? _____

✓ Skill Check

Word Check   Northern Hemisphere   Equator   degrees
                  Southern Hemisphere   latitude

Write the word on the line that makes each sentence true.

1. The Equator divides the globe into the _____

   _____ and the _____ .

2. The _____ is at 0° latitude.

Map Check

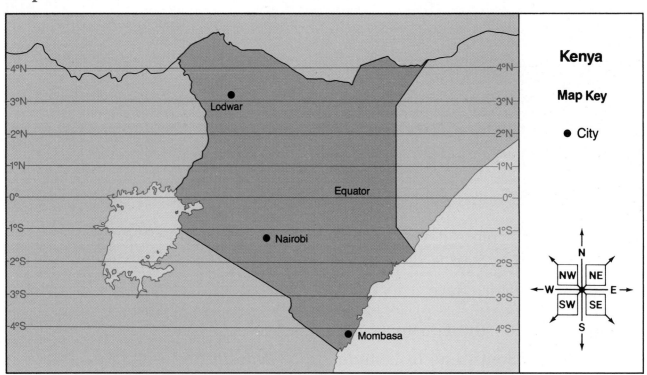

1. Trace the 3°N latitude line in green.

   What city is near that line? _____

2. Trace the 1°S latitude line in orange.

   What city is near that line? _____

3. Trace the 4°S latitude line in red.

   What city is near that line? _____

Longitude

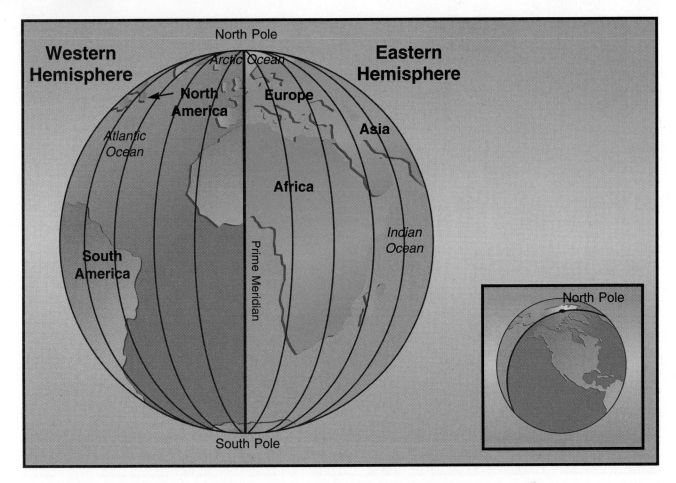

Another important line on the globe is the **Prime Meridian.** It is an imaginary line that goes from the North Pole to the South Pole.

Find the Prime Meridian in both pictures above. The Prime Meridian divides the globe into two hemispheres. Half the globe east of the Prime Meridian is the **Eastern Hemisphere.** Half the globe west of the Prime Meridian is the **Western Hemisphere.**

► Find the land in the Eastern Hemisphere.
It is colored green.
What continents are in the Eastern Hemisphere?
What oceans are in the Eastern Hemisphere?

► Find the land in the Western Hemisphere.
It is colored brown.
You can see part of three continents. What are they?
What oceans are in the Western Hemisphere?

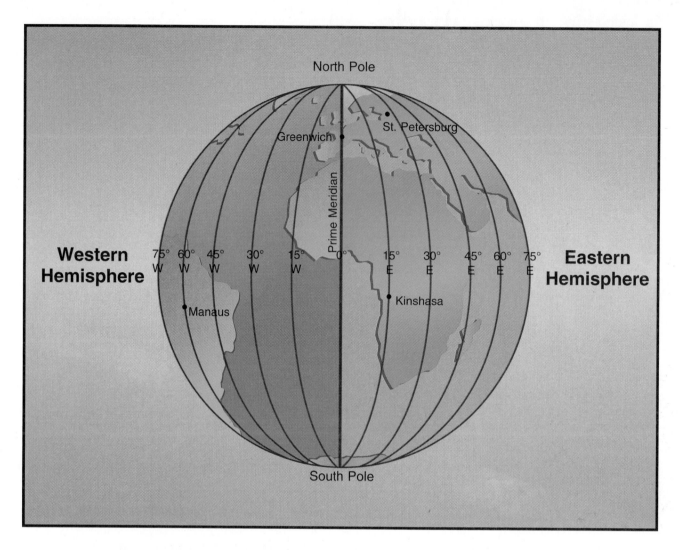

Find the Prime Meridian on the globe above. Now find the curved lines on each side of the Prime Meridian. These are called **lines of longitude**. Why are these lines curved?

We use lines of longitude to locate places east and west of the Prime Meridian. The lines are numbered and marked by degrees. The symbol ° stands for degrees. The Prime Meridian is at 0° longitude.

► Find the 15°E longitude line.
   What does the letter E stand for?
   What city is at 15°East?

► Find the 60°W longitude line.
   What does the letter W stand for?
   What city is at 60°West?

► Find St. Petersburg.
   What line of longitude is it near?

Finding Longitude

This map shows part of England.

1. Color England green between 1°E and 2°E.

   What city lies in that area? _____

2. Color England brown between 1°W and 2°W.

   What city lies in that area? _____

3. Color England yellow between 2°W and 3°W.

   What city lies in that area? _____

4. Color England orange between 4°W and 5°W.

   What city lies in that area? _____

5. What city lies on the Prime Meridian? _____

Finding Longitude

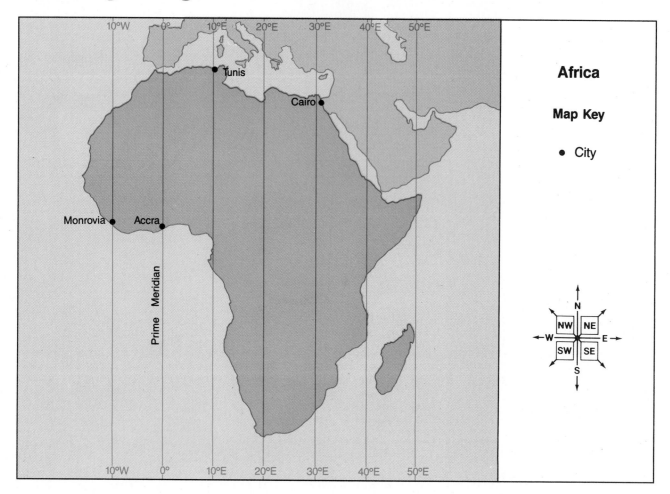

You can find a place if you know which line of longitude it is on.

Study the map of Africa above.

1. Find the Prime Meridian. Trace it in red.

   What city is on the Prime Meridian? _____

2. Find the 10°West line of longitude. Trace it in green.

   What city is at 10°West? _____

3. Find the 10°East line of longitude. Trace it in purple.

   What city is at 10°East? _____

4. Find the 30°East line of longitude. Trace it in orange.

   What city is near 30°East? _____

Skill Check

Word Check   **Eastern Hemisphere**   **Prime Meridian**
                           Western Hemisphere   **lines of longitude**

Write the word on the line that makes each sentence true.

1. _____ measure how far east or west a place is.

2. The _____ is at 0° longitude.

3. The Prime Meridian divides the globe into the _____

_____ and the _____.

Map Check

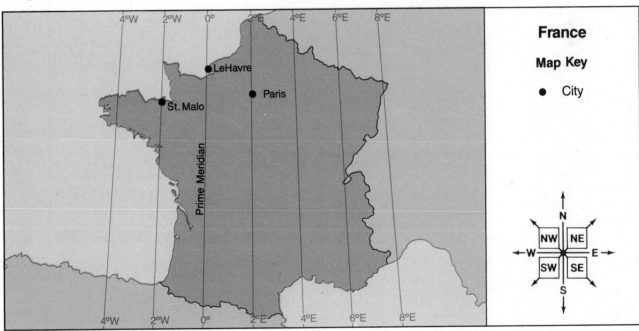

1. Trace the Prime Meridian in green.

   What city is on that line? _____

2. Trace the 2°W longitude line in orange.

   What city is on that line? _____

3. Trace the 2°E longitude line in red.

   What city is on that line? _____

Location describes where places are found. You can tell the location of a place by what it is near or what is around it. The map below shows Gabon, a country in Africa.

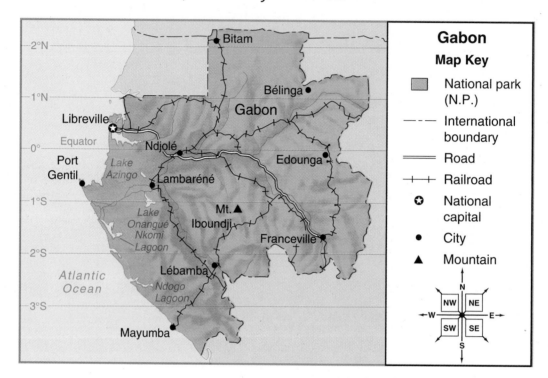

1. Find the Equator (0°) on the map. Trace it in red. What cities are located nearest to the Equator?

   _____

2. Find the capital city of Libreville on the map. Circle it. Describe the location of Libreville.

   _____

   _____

3. What point of interest is located between 0° and 2° S latitude?

   _____

4. Trace the 0° longitude line in green on the map. What is another name for this line of longitude? Add this name to the map.

_____

5. What line of longitude is nearest to Madrid, Spain?

_____

6. Find the capital of Portugal. Name this city and the line of longitude it is near.

_____

7. Which city in Spain is nearest to the Prime Meridian, Valencia or Barcelona?

_____

8. Which city in Spain is located near 8°W longitude?

_____

Books Read During Room 10's Reading Contest

📖 **stands for one book**

Diego	📖 📖 📖 📖 📖 📖
Sarah	📖 📖 📖 📖 📖
Ayako	📖 📖 📖 📖
Sam	📖 📖

Some students in Room 10 had a reading contest. They made a **pictograph** to keep track of the number of books they read. A pictograph shows facts using symbols.

Follow these steps to read a pictograph.

1. <u>Read the title.</u> This pictograph shows _____

   _____ .

2. <u>Read the key.</u> Each symbol on this graph stands for

   _____ .

3. <u>Read the words at the left of the graph.</u> Who read books

   in this contest? _____ _____ _____ _____

4. <u>Read the longest row of symbols first.</u> Diego read

   _____ books.

5. <u>Read the other rows.</u> Write the number of books each student

   read. Sarah _____   Ayako _____   Sam _____

6. <u>Compare the rows.</u> Use <u>more</u> or <u>fewer</u>.

   Sarah read _____ books than Ayako.

   Sam read _____ books than Sarah.

   Diego read _____ books than Ayako.

Aluminum Cans Collected at Mendez School
▯ stands for 10 pounds of aluminum cans

Second Grade	▯ ▯ ▯
Third Grade	
Fourth Grade	
Fifth Grade	
Sixth Grade	

Students at Mendez School were raising money for a new playscape. They collected aluminum cans to sell at the recycling center. They made a pictograph to keep track of the pounds of cans they collected. Follow these steps to finish the pictograph.

1. This pictograph will show _____

_____.

2. Each symbol will stand for _____.

3. The groups who collected cans are the _____,

_____, _____,

_____, and _____.

4. Finish the pictograph. Here are the pounds of cans each grade collected:

Second Grade	30	Fifth Grade	40
Third Grade	60	Sixth Grade	50
Fourth Grade	40		

Draw one symbol for every 10 pounds of aluminum cans.

5. Compare the rows. The most cans were collected by the

_____. The fewest cans were collected by the

_____. The _____ and the

_____ collected the same amount of cans.

Reading a Bar Graph

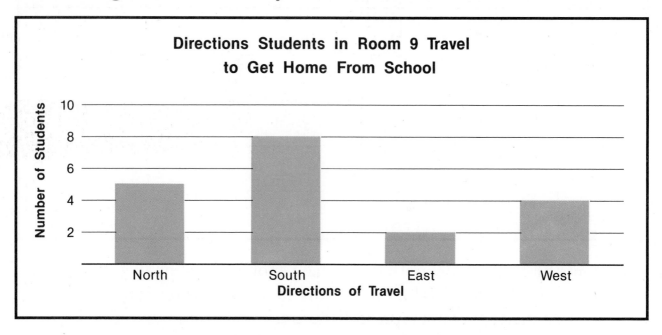

**Directions Students in Room 9 Travel
to Get Home From School**

The students in Room 9 travel in several directions to get home from school. This bar graph shows how many students go in each direction. A **bar graph** is a graph that uses bars to stand for numbers. Follow these steps to read and use a bar graph.

1. Read the title. This bar graph shows _____

   _____ .

2. Read the words at the bottom of each bar. The bars on this

   graph show _____ .

3. Read the words and numbers at the left side of the graph.

   Each number on the graph stands for _____ .

4. Read the tallest bar. Put your finger at the top of the bar.
   Move it across the line to the left. Read the number there.

   _____ people go south to get home from school.

5. How many go north? _____ west? _____ east? _____

6. Compare the bars. Most of the students in Room 9 go _____

   to get home. The fewest students go _____ .

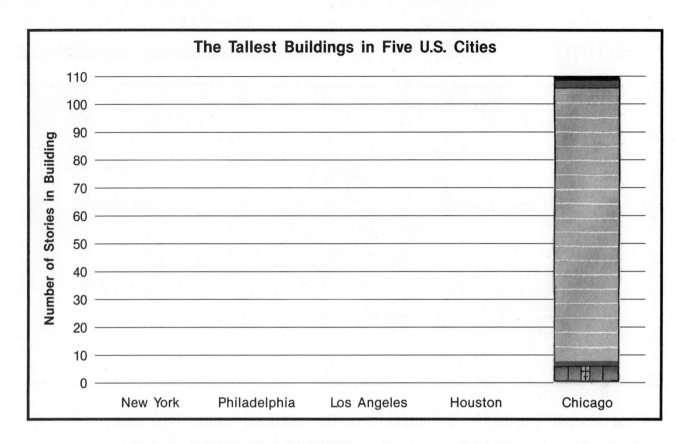

The Tallest Buildings in Five U.S. Cities

Number of Stories in Building

110, 100, 90, 80, 70, 60, 50, 40, 30, 20, 10, 0

New York   Philadelphia   Los Angeles   Houston   Chicago

Which U.S. city has the tallest building?
Follow these steps to finish this bar graph.

1. This bar graph will show _____

   _____.

2. The bars on this graph will show buildings in the cities of

   _____, _____, _____,

   _____, and _____.

3. The tallest building in Chicago has _____ stories.

4. Finish the graph. Here are the number of stories in each city's
   tallest building: Philadelphia 61; Los Angeles 73;
   Houston 75; New York 110.

5. Compare the bars. The shortest of these buildings is in

   _____. The two tallest buildings are in

   _____ and _____.

Reading a Circle Graph

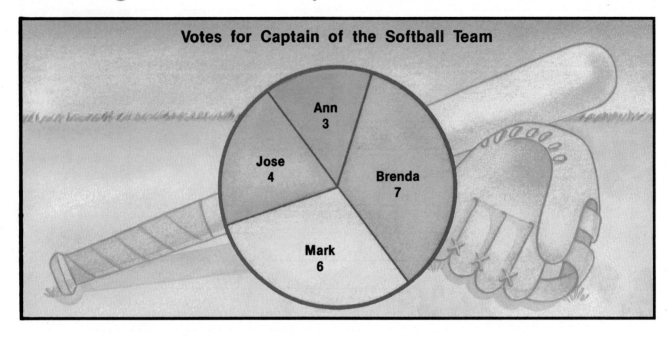

Votes for Captain of the Softball Team

Ann 3

Jose 4

Brenda 7

Mark 6

Four people wanted to be captain of the softball team. The team took a vote. This circle graph shows how the votes were divided. A **circle graph** shows how something whole is divided into parts. Follow these steps to read and use a circle graph. Finish each step.

1. Read the title. The whole circle stands for _____

   _____ .

2. Read the biggest part of the circle. Who received the most

   votes? _____

3. Read the other pieces of the circle. Read clockwise around the circle from the biggest piece. The pieces get smaller as you go.

   Who received the fewest votes? _____

4. Compare the pieces. To be team captain, the winner has to receive at least half the votes.

   How many votes were there in all? _____

   Did anyone receive half of the votes? _____

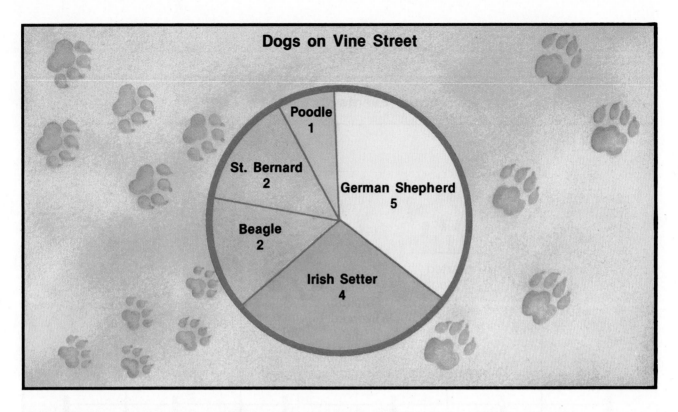

Dogs on Vine Street

Poodle 1

German Shepherd 5

St. Bernard 2

Beagle 2

Irish Setter 4

Clifford counted the dogs on his street. This circle graph shows how many of each kind of dog he counted.

1. <u>Read the title.</u> The whole circle stands for _____

_____ .

2. <u>Read the biggest part of the circle.</u> There are more

_____ than any other kind of dog.

<u>Read the other pieces of the circle.</u> Read clockwise around the circle from the biggest piece.

3. There is the same number of _____ and

_____ .

<u>Compare the pieces.</u> Finish each sentence. Use <u>more</u> or <u>fewer</u>.

4. There are _____ poodles than any other dog.

5. There are _____ St. Bernards than German shepherds.

6. _____ Irish setters live on Vine Street than beagles.

Reading a Time Line

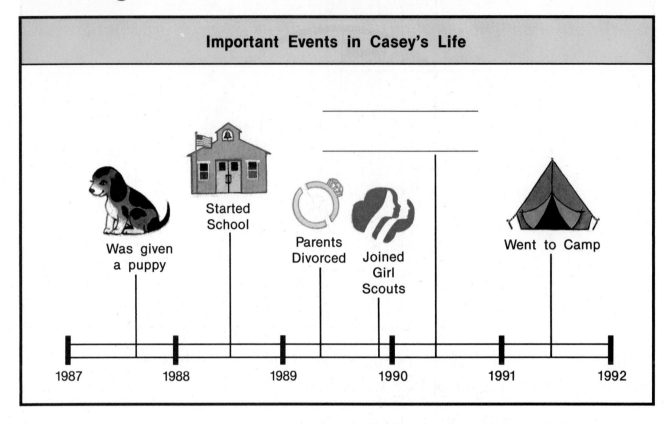

Important Events in Casey's Life

Was given a puppy

Started School

Parents Divorced

Joined Girl Scouts

Went to Camp

1987   1988   1989   1990   1991   1992

A **time line** is a line that shows a number of years. Marks on the line stand for events, or things that happened, during those years. The events are marked in the order they happened. Follow these steps to read a time line.

1. Read the title. This time line shows _____

   _____ .

2. Read the dates along the bottom of the time line. This

   time line begins in _____ and ends in _____ .

3. Study the order of events on the time line. Write before or after.

   Casey went to camp _____ she got a puppy.

   Casey's parents divorced _____ she joined Girl Scouts.

4. Add to the time line. In 1990 Casey started cello lessons. Write "Started cello lessons" on the line in 1990.

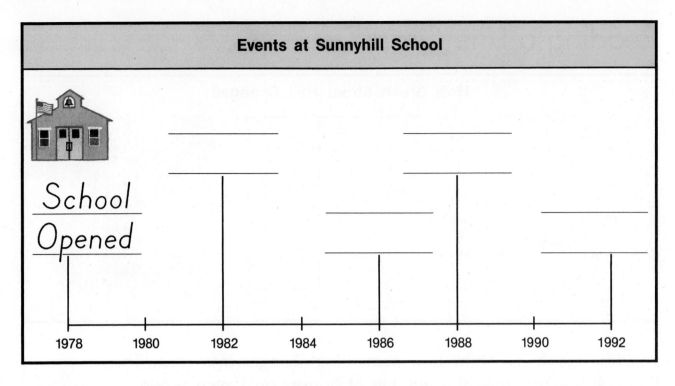

Events at Sunnyhill School

School
Opened

1978 1980 1982 1984 1986 1988 1990 1992

Casey is writing a report about things that happened at her school since it opened in 1978. She wants to show them on a time line. Follow the steps to finish the time line.

1. Read the title. This time line shows _____.

2. Read the dates along the bottom of the time line. This

   time line begins in _____ and ends in _____.

3. Put the events in order. Number these events from 1 to 5, in the order they happened.

   _____ 1988 New lunch menu

   _____ 1982 School caught fire

   _____ 1992 Astronaut visited

   _____ 1986 Pool built

   _____ 1978 School opened

4. Write the events in order on the time line. Write each event on the line above the year it happened. The first event is written for you.

Reading a Line Graph

A **line graph** can show how something changes over time. This line graph shows how the number of houses on Green Street changed. Follow these steps to read a line graph.

1. <u>Read the title.</u> This line graph shows _____

   _____ .

2. <u>Read the dates along the bottom of the graph.</u>
   Read from left to right. This graph shows how things

   changed between the years of _____ and _____ .

3. <u>Read the words and numbers on the left side of the graph.</u>

   The numbers stand for _____ .

4. <u>Read the dots on the line.</u> Put your finger on the dot above
   1980. Slide it to the left to read the number of houses
   on Green Street that year.

   In 1980 there were _____ houses on Green Street.

   In 1984 there were _____ houses on Green Street.

5. <u>Study the shape of the line.</u> Does it go up or down? The
   line shows that the number of houses on Green Street has

   grown _____ every year since 1980.
          _{greater/smaller}

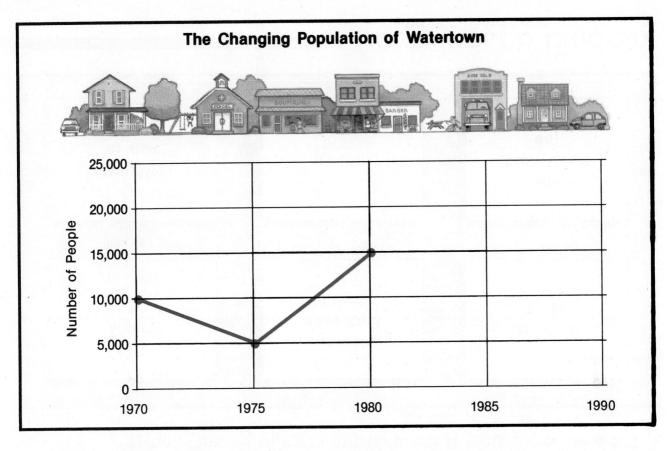

The Changing Population of Watertown

This line graph shows how the population of Watertown has changed over time. Follow the steps to finish the line graph. How has the population changed?

1. This line graph shows _____

_____.

2. This graph will show how the population changed between

the years of _____ and _____.

3. In 1970 there were _____ people in Watertown.

In 1975 there were _____. In 1980 there were _____.

4. Finish the line. In 1985 the population was 20,000. In 1990 the population was 25,000. Add dots for 1985 and 1990. Connect the dots to complete the line.

5. Did the population of Watertown grow greater or smaller

between 1975 and 1990? _____

Reading a Flow Chart

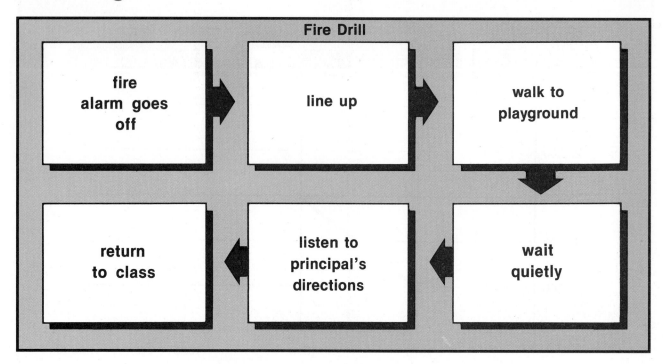

Suppose your school is having a fire drill. To be safe, you must follow some important steps. A **flow chart** is a drawing that shows the steps for doing or making something. Follow these steps to read a flow chart.

1. Read the title. This flow chart shows the steps for

   _____ .

2. Read the steps. Follow the arrows. Start at the top left

   corner. The first step in the fire drill is _____

   _____ .

   The last step is _____ .

3. Study the order of the steps.

   Walk to the playground before you _____ .

   Line up after _____ .

   Listen to the principal's directions after you _____ .

   Walk to the playground after you _____ .

How to make a peanut butter and jelly sandwich

1. Get out the bread, peanut butter, and jelly.

2. _____

3. Spread peanut butter on one piece of bread.

4. _____

5. Put the two pieces of bread together.

6. _____

7. _____

Some of the steps have been left out of this flow chart. Follow the directions to read and finish it.

1. This flow chart shows how to _____

_____.

2. The first step in making a peanut butter and jelly sandwich

is to _____.

3. Add these missing steps to the flow chart above.
   (2.) Get a knife.
   (4.) Spread jelly on another piece of bread.
   (6.) Put everything away.
   (7.) Eat it!

4. Study the order of the steps.

Before you put the two pieces of bread together you must

_____.

The last step in making a peanut butter and jelly sandwich

is to _____.

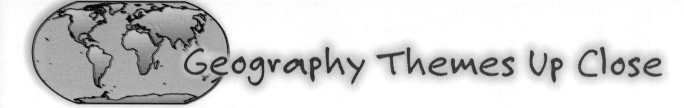

Human/Environment Interaction describes how people live in their environment. The environment has resources people can use. Where there is rich soil, people can farm. People use rivers and lakes for water, for fun, and for travel.

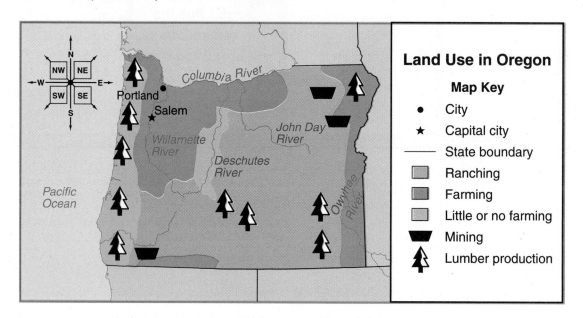

1. Where is most of the farming done in Oregon?

   _____

2. In what parts of Oregon do people grow trees for lumber?

   _____

3. Where is mining done in Oregon?

   _____

4. Write a sentence that describes how people in Oregon live in their environment.

   _____

   _____

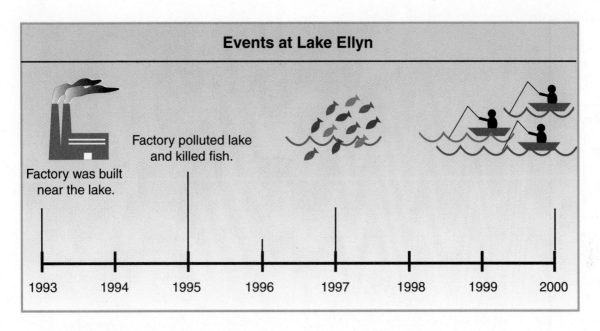

Events at Lake Ellyn

Factory was built near the lake.

Factory polluted lake and killed fish.

1993 1994 1995 1996 1997 1998 1999 2000

5. Name two ways Lake Ellyn changed in 1995.

_____

_____

6. Add the following events to the time line. Write each event in order on the time line.
   In 2000 Lake Ellyn held a fishing derby.
   In 1996 Lake Ellyn was cleaned.
   In 1997 new fish were put into Lake Ellyn.

7. Look at the time line. Explain one way people changed the environment of Lake Ellyn.

_____

_____

_____

THE UNITED STATES
Map Key

National Boundary ——— State Boundary
National Capital ⊛ ★ State Capital

0 100 200 300 400 500 MI
0 100 200 300 400 500 600 700 800 KM

70°N 80°N 80°N 70°N

Arctic Ocean

180°
160°W
140°W
120°W
100°W
80°W
60°W
40°W
20°W
0°

Greenland

(U.S.)

60°N

Pacific Ocean

Canada

Hudson Bay

50°N

Ottawa

Great Lakes

40°N

United States

Washington, D.C.

Atlantic Ocean

30°N

N
NW NE
W   E
SW SE
S

Gulf of Mexico

Bahamas

U.S. Virgin Islands

20°N

Mexico

Cuba

Haiti

Puerto Rico

Dominican Republic

Jamaica

Mexico City

Belize

Guatemala

Honduras

Caribbean Sea

El Salvador

Nicaragua

10°N

NORTH AMERICA

Costa Rica

0   200   400   600 MI

Panama

0   200 400 600 800 KM

120°W   110°W   100°W   90°W   80°W   70°W

THE WORLD

Pacific Ocean

Australia

Asia

Indian Ocean

Europe

Africa

Prime Meridian

Antarctica

Atlantic Ocean

South America

North America

Arctic Ocean

Equator

Pacific Ocean

N
NW NE
W · E
SW SE
S

THE WORLD

1000   2000 MI

1000 2000 3000 KM

Glossary

bar graph (p. 64) a graph with thick lines, or bars, of different lengths to compare numbers or amounts

circle graph (p. 66) a circle that shows how something whole is divided into parts

coast (p. 28) the land next to the ocean

compass rose (p. 8) a symbol that shows the directions: north, south, east, and west

continent (p. 50) a very large body of land

degrees (p. 51) the unit of measurement used for lines of latitude and longitude

distance (p. 14) how far one place is from another

Eastern Hemisphere (p. 55) the half of Earth east of the Prime Meridian

environment (p. 5) the land, water, and air around you. It is the plant and animal life, too.

Equator (p. 50) the imaginary line that goes around the middle of Earth. The Equator divides Earth into the Northern and Southern Hemispheres.

factory (p. 22) a place where resources are made into other things

flow chart (p. 72) a drawing that shows steps for doing or making something

geography (p. 4) about Earth and how people live and work on Earth

grid (p. 42) a pattern of lines that cross each other to form squares

gulf (p. 28) a large body of water that cuts deep into the land

hemisphere (p. 50) half of the globe or half of Earth. The four hemispheres are Northern, Southern, Eastern, and Western.

human/environment interaction (p. 5, 74) explains how people live in their environment

human features (p. 4) things such as houses, roads, bridges, schools, farms, and factories that people make

intermediate directions (p. 11) northeast, southeast, southwest, northwest

interstate highway (p. 38) a highway that crosses the entire country

kilometers (p. 14) a metric unit of length for measuring distance. Also written **KM** and km.

landform map (p. 28) a map that shows the shape of the land, such as mountains and hills

line graph (p. 70) a graph that shows how something changes over time

lines of latitude (p. 51)   lines that circle Earth north and south of the Equator. They are numbered and marked by degrees.

lines of longitude (p. 56)   lines that circle Earth from the North Pole to the South Pole. They are numbered and marked by degrees.

location (p. 4, 60)   tells where something can be found

map (p. 8)   a drawing of a real place

map index (p. 43)   the alphabetical list of places on a map with their grid squares

map key (p. 8)   the guide to what the symbols on a map stand for

map scale (p. 14) the guide to what the distances on a map stand for

miles (p. 14)   a unit of length used in measuring distance. Also written **MI** or mi.

mountain range (p. 31)   a group or chain of mountains

movement (p. 6, 48)   describes how people, goods, information, and ideas get from place to place

Northern Hemisphere (p. 50)   the half of Earth north of the Equator

physical features (p. 4)   are things from nature, such as bodies of water, landforms, weather, plants, and animals

pictograph (p. 62)   a way to show and compare facts using symbols

place (p. 4, 20)   tells what a location is like

plains (p. 28)   large areas of flat lands

plateau (p. 28)   high, flat land

Prime Meridian (p. 55)   the line of longitude from the South Pole to the North Pole measured at 0°. It divides Earth into Eastern and Western Hemispheres.

regions (p. 7, 34)   areas that have something in common

resources (p. 22)   things people can use, such as oil, lumber, and water

route (p. 36)   a road or path from one place to another. Highways, railroads, and trails are routes.

Southern Hemisphere (p. 50)   the half of Earth south of the Equator

state highway (p. 38)   a main road that connects cities and towns within the boundaries of one state

symbol (p. 8)   a picture on a map that stands for something real

time line (p. 68)   a line that shows a number of years and the events that happened in order

U.S. highway (p. 37)   a main highway that passes through more than one state

Western Hemisphere (p. 55)   the half of Earth west of the Prime Meridian